COLORED BY:_____

Art by Charles Schulz

Dalmatian Press, LLC, 2011. All rights reserved. Printed in the U.S.A.
The DALMATIAN PRESS name and logo are trademarks of Dalmatian Publishing Group,
Franklin, Tennessee 37067. 1-866-418-2572. No part of this book may be reproduced or
copied in any form without written permission from the copyright owner. CE13983

HERE IT COMES, LUCY—RIGHT AT YOU!

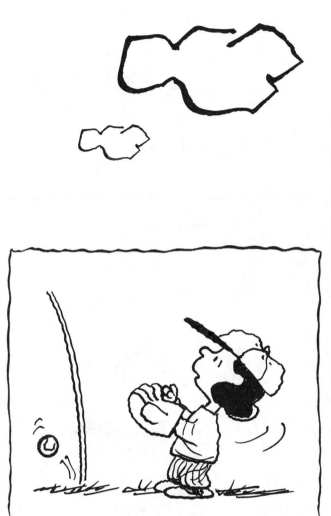

PLOP!

PLOP!

ONE MORE TRY...

PLOP!

GOOD GRIEF!

"I'M NOT SURE BEETHOVEN IS ALL HE'S CRACKED UP TO BE."

SCHROEDER IS QUITE SURE.

"WHY DO I HAVE TO HAVE SUCH A SILLY SISTER?"

"EVEN MY DOG DRIVES ME NUTS."

SOMETIMES ONE GOOD YAWN. . .

. . .LEADS TO ANOTHER.

"C'MON, CHARLIE BROWN. YOU CAN DO IT!"

GOOD GRIEF!

HERE COMES A SLOW BALL TO PIGPEN. . . .

. . .AND A FAST ONE BACK TO THE MOUND!

"SEEMS LIKE A GOOD DAY TO FLY A KITE."

"WELL, MAYBE NOT."

THE KITE-EATING TREE STRIKES AGAIN.

GOOD GRIEF, CHARLIE BROWN!

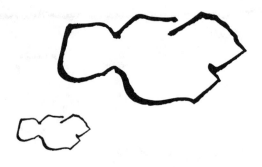

GO, TEAM!

CHARLIE BROWN TAKES THE KICK. . .

. . .FOR THE WINNING GOAL!

THE CHAMPS

GOOD GOING, CHARLIE BROWN!